Things in My House

By Joe Kaufman

gb **GOLDEN PRESS**

Western Publishing Company, Inc.
Racine, Wisconsin

Eighth Printing, 1977

There are all kinds
of things in my house:

a hammer,

a shoe,

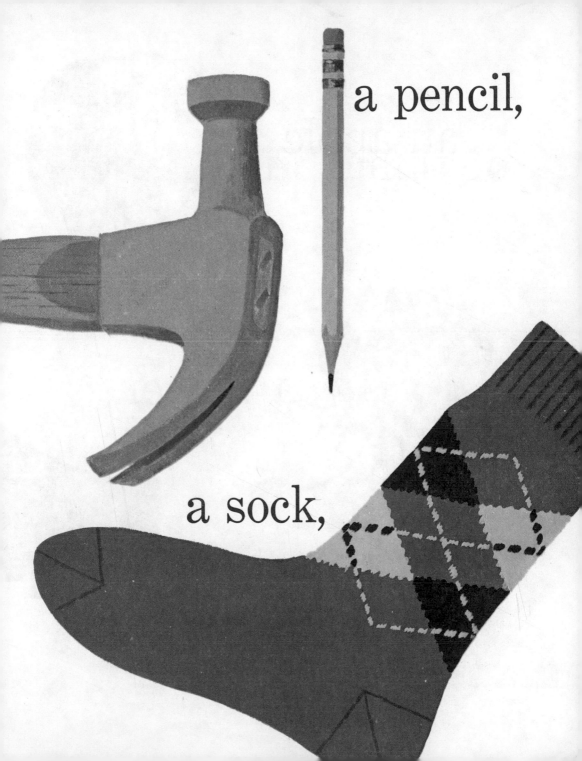

a pencil,

a sock,

an apple,

a flower,

a fork,

and a clock.

A saw,

a leaf,

a ball,

a bat,

an umbrella,

glasses,

a block,

and a hat.

A kettle,

a lemon,

a glove,

a toy boat,

a toothbrush,

a ruler,

	1		2		3		4		5		6

a horn,

and a coat.

A candle,

a doll,

a cookie,

a nail,

a locomotive,

an onion,

a shovel, and a pail.

A fireman's hat,

a walnut,

a lamp,

scissors,

a cup,

a brush,

and a stamp.

An airplane,

a puppet,

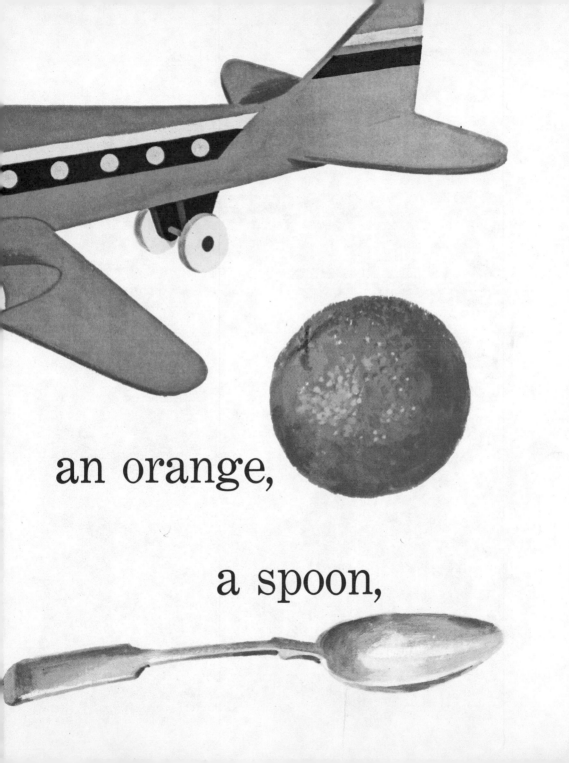

an orange,

a spoon,

a window,

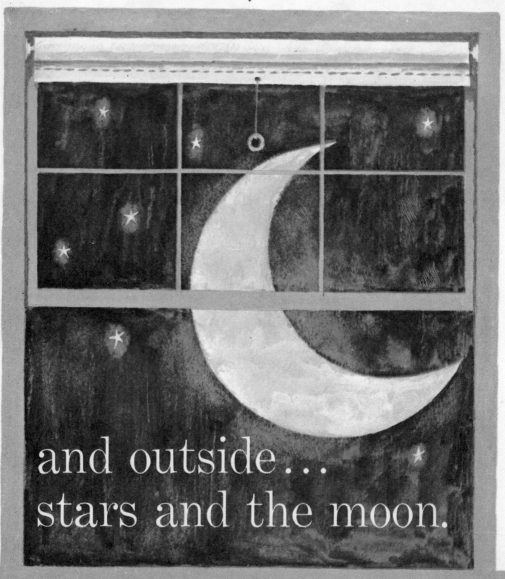

and outside…
stars and the moon.